A SCOTTISH BESTIARY OF OLD

1710

A Treasury of Scottish Myth and Legend

BOOK I – THE GREAT CLAN CHIEF SERIES

MIRROR AND COMB PUBLISHING

For Talorcan,
King of the Picts
Always see and believe in
the magic of Scotland.

First Published in 2015 by Mirror and Comb Publishing. All rights reserved.
No part of the contents of this book may be produced without written
permission of the publisher.

All text and images are copyright

Text copyright © 2018 by Belle Robertson

Illustrations copyright © 2018 by Larry MacDougall

Book and cover design by Raspberry Creative Type, Edinburgh

Mirror and Comb Publishing, Edinburgh

ISBN 978-0-9574990-1-0

This sketchbook belongs to the Great Clan Chieftain, if found, please return to my castle in Scotland.

Dear Fellow Antiquarians,

After a lifetime's fascination with Scottish myth and legend, I have compiled a bestiary of beasties native to this land. Over mountain and glen, I have searched far and wide for our elusive creatures. Some you will know well, others linger still in the dark.

From the Islands and Highlands to the Central and Border Lands, as Clan Chieftain, I have travelled all across Scotland. By open fire and dram in hand, I have listened intently to many a Clan Chieftain tale.

In this Celtic land of legend, epic landscape and history, I have discovered a country brimming with myth and our fairy lore I wish to preserve the myths and ancient traditions for future generations. Now in my elder years, I acknowledge the importance of documenting my knowledge and experience. I wish to preserve the myths and fragments of oral history for future generations.

My descriptions are illustrated with sketches from memory and recorded sightings.

Believe what you may, I seek only to provide a record of the beasts and otherworldly creatures that roam this ancient land.

Please note all footnotes are historically accurate.

John, Lord Dunteviot,
Great Clan Chieftain
of Scotland

5TH June 1710

SHETLAND
ISLAND

ORKNEY ISLAND

Eijnhallow Island

Isle of Hoy

Sandwood Bay, North West

Minch, Outer Hebrides

North Uist

Dunvegan Castle, Skye

Beinn Mhor
South Uist

Slains Castle, Cruden Bay, Aberdeenshire

Bennachie

Loch Morar, Lochaber

Fortingall

Pitlochry, Perthshire

Glen Etive

x Schiehallion

Huntingtowerfield Castle

Ardnadrochit, Mull

Ben Venue, Trossachs

Stirling Castle

Edinburgh Castle

Linton

Hermitage Castle, Borders

Bladnoch, Dumfries

x marks geographical centre of
Scotland – Mount Schiehallion –
Robertson Treasure

Unicorn

There is mention of 'historie of the unicorne' tapestries from the Royal Collection inventories at Stirling dating to 1539.

Following the Union of the Crowns in 1603, King James VI of Scotland altered the Scottish coat of arms by replacing a unicorn with a lion to represent Britain.

The lufare unicorne
That voidis venym with his euoure
horne.
King James I
(The Kingis Quair – 15th century)

To begin, we claim the legendary unicorn as our own. Of great strength, courageous and pure, this is our ancient emblem royal. Linked with the House of Stewart, the royal arms and seals of Scotland were long supported by unicorns rampant. With great honour, I present our national animal supreme.

The royal residence of Stirling Castle is historically associated with the medieval unicorn. Long ago, a magnificent set of French tapestries depicting the 'Hunt for the Unicorn' furnished the chambers of King James V. Much loved by his young daughter, Marie Stuart, future Queen of Scots, she was captivated by the story of the creature's extinction. Expertly woven in gold and sumptuous colour, it depicts the unicorn's violent persecution to attain its prized horn – the alicorn.

With powers of purification, the magic spiralled horn was revered for its ability to neutralise poison. Kings and Queens exchanged chests of gold for the precious treasure.

The gold-mounted Stuart Alicorn of Stirling has now been lost. They say a royal unicorn will always guard the infant Stuart heir.

For to test a real alicorn, place in cold water, if boils and remains cold, behold the prized treasure.

Dwarfie Stane

The Dwarfie Stane is thought to be the
only Neolithic rock-cut chambered tomb in
Britain and dates back to c.3000 BC.

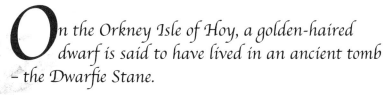

On the Orkney Isle of Hoy, a golden-haired dwarf is said to have lived in an ancient tomb – the Dwarfie Stane.

In his 'Descriptio Insularum Orchadiarum' (1529), Jo Ben described this archaeological curiosity as being constructed by a giant and his wife. However, upon inspection of this ancient site, I found two small stone bed recesses visible through the tiny doorway confirming the dwelling of a dwarf-sized creature.

Alive in local memory, the dwarf is remembered as spending a great deal of time combing the beaches for fossils. Yet to be discovered, his treasure is buried near the stane.

Now the shepherds tend to stay clear of the place. For in moonlight and rain, he occasionally appears by the entrance inspecting his precious fossils. Fossils as old as the tomb – as old as himself.

But I would rather think, feeing it could not accommodate any of a Gigantick ftature, that it might be for the ufe of fome Dwarf, as the Name feems to import
(John Brand, 'A New Description of Orkney' – 1703)

Kelpie

The kelpie, a shapeshifting waterhorse, dwells by Scotland's rivers and streams. Known to flood waters, it will offer passage to travellers across the torrents. But once you have jumped a kelpie, there is no escape. Locked in its fur, glued to its back, you will be dragged into the depths of the water.

A kelpie will take two forms. A wild horse with a constantly dripping mane or a handsome man with long matted seaweed hair. However, by the time you have recognised the characteristics, it will be too late.

If you are weary of travel, in need of some rest, never approach a lone horse or a young man beckoning you to the water. Beware, too many have been taken.

Catching a kelpie is only possible by taking control of its golden bridle. Many Scottish castles have been built upon the slaving of a kelpie, but the clan seat will always remain cursed. It is believed the House of Morphie (Kincardineshire) was built by an enslaved kelpie, now only the ruins and an old yew tree exist!

Stay away from the Clachan an tacharain (Ford of Kelpie) on Islay.

If Kelpie gets you by its claw,
Light a torch, don't touch its fur.
Don't listen to its screeching cry,
And never stare it in the eye.

Through mist, the wildest
of horses, jet black fur, fire
in its eyes. Grazing by
water edge, offers its aid,
beware, beware a kelpie
stands there!

Dunvegan Fairy

On the Isle of Skye, locked within a great chest in Dunvegan Castle, there lies a large piece of tattered silk. This prized possession of Clan MacLeod is known as the Fairy Flag.

Long ago the Clan Chief fell in love with a most beautiful Celtic fairy princess, a creature of dance and music. They married and lived together in the Castle, but after twenty years she was forced to return to Fairyland. When she departed at the place known as Fairy Bridge, she left her love a precious gift, a section of her wedding dress. This flag could protect the Chief and Clan in battle, but could only be unfurled and waved three times. Now there only remains one last chance to protect the Clan.

The flag was entrusted to a family of hereditary standard bearers, but the male line has since died out.

Acquiring a section of the flag will bestow magical properties. Now a faded rag, it was once described as 'wrought in gold with red elf spots all across'.

The Dunvegan Fairy will appear once more to protect the clan, but if her flag is ever destroyed or lost, the fairy princess can never return.

The MacLeod standard bearers were honoured
with burial within the Clan MacLeod Chief
tomb at the Abbey of Iona, the resting place of
Scottish kings. Subsequent burials were offered
at St Clement's Church, Rodel, Isle of Harris.

Cailleach

The Cailleach is the giantess of the Scottish Highlands. She is guardian of vast forests and wild animals. But never rile her, the old hag of winter will flood glens and freeze the ground with her massive staff. Hunters take heed: if you catch her unaware or bathing, no prey will you catch.

Across the land she has several mountain homes. Her favourite dwelling is the magnificent Ben Cruachan overlooking Loch Awe. She accidently created the loch when her well above the mountain overflowed. This is her haven. She always returns to this place as the loch keeps her treasure trove safe.

To hear the song of the Cailleach across the hills is enchantment itself; few have heard the haunting melody.

Every year, the Cailleach must travel to Coire Bhreacain (Cauldron of the Plaid), the great whirlpool of Corryvreckan in the Hebrides. In the swirlin' powerful waves, she washes her massive yellow plaid to summon the cold winds, Scotia's winter Goddess.

She was last seen in the Trossachs in 1700. Now of great age, not the strong athletic Amazonian she once was.

Cailleach translates as 'Old Woman' in Scots Gaelic.

The Corryvrechan whirlpool is one of the largest in the world. It lies in the Corryvrechan Gulf between the Isles of Jura and Scarba, Argyll & Bute.

I have heard of a shrine in Glen Cailliche at Glen Lyon known as Tigh na Cailliche. It contains three strange-shaped stones thought to represent, the Cailleach, the Bodach (husband) and the Nighean (daughter). A gift from the Cailleach, the stones must be taken out at Beltane (spring) and replaced at Samhain (winter), thus ensuring the fertility of the glen.

I wonder if she is still out there sitting amongst the hills, our Mountain Queen.

White Stag

*I*n 1128 King David I was hunting on the feast of the Holy Cross (Rood) on the lands below Arthur's Seat in Edinburgh. Chasing a white stag he fell and was charged by his prey. As the antler transformed into a large cross, he was saved from the trampling hooves. On the site of the miracle, King David built a church dedicated to the Holy Cross, the Abbey of Holyrood.

To see a white hart nestled in the mist, darting through the trees, is rare indeed. An omen of change, to behold the majestic messenger is a wondrous sight. It is said if a white stag is ever seen on an estate, it will foretell the death of the Clan Chief. I hope I don't see one too soon!

Although the antlers of a white stag are greatly prized, never hunt down the sacred beast, no good will ever come of it.

Like the horn of a unicorn, the golden footprint of the mythical white stag has magical properties. To find one is very rare, to my knowledge only one has been discovered and it's in my possession!

This legend is preserved upon the great seal of the Canongate. Dating to the 16th century, it contains a miniature depiction of stag antlers crossed.

Boobrie

In 1600, the House of Ruthven was seized by
James VI after a plot to kill him by the 3rd
Earl of Ruthven. The estate was gifted to
the Murrays of Tullibardine and was known
thereafter as Huntingtower Castle.

A bird of terrifying nature, the boobrie is the mythical waterbird of the Highlands.

This gigantic bird with markings of white and gold has massive wings, talons of steel and short muscular legs.

It is the metamorphosed form of the waterhorse (Each Uisage) and the water bull (Tarbh Uisg). Its call is a deep bellow and its natural habitat is remote lochs and glens. It preys on cattle, humans and golden eagles.

If the boobrie spots you from the air, take cover quickly in a neuk that its huge talons cannot reach.

Huntingtower Castle is said to own a prized specimen, a stuffed boobrie perched upon a branch of gold. John Murray, Duke of Atholl, swears a deep roar is often heard echoing throughout the stone walls.

Ghillie Dhu

*T*he Ghillie Dhu, the 'dark-haired lad', is the most ancient of Scotland's fairies, stemming from the mists of time.

These solitary creatures dwell in remote woods. They are the chosen guardians of precious forests and trees.

These tiny beings, clothed in moss and leaves are notoriously shy, but occasionally appear to children. They can often be summoned by the playing of a certain air on the clarsach, the name of which has been long lost.

A great many once thrived in the Caledonian Forest. A few still protect the Black Wood of Rannoch, the remnant of the ancient pine forest that once covered Scotland, but numbers have dwindled.

One is said to reside in the Fortingall Yew, Scotland's eternal tree. Guarding the tree and its ancient secret, this Ghillie Dhu is as old as the tree itself, some say over three thousand years.

The Fortingall Yew (Taxus baccata) in Highland Perthshire is one of Britain's oldest trees, estimated at around two to five thousand years old. Its trunk measures almost 57 feet in girth.

Shelleycoat

Have you ever heard of the Shelleycoat of Leith? A wailing tricky wee thing, a water creature you often hear, but never want to see. One is said to dwell around the shores of Edinburgh's busy harbour where its menacing laugh is often heard in the dark waves.

A strange creature covered in shells, the rattling of its coat is often heard near the water, its haunt being a large rock accessible when the tide is low. It is known to play tricks on the locals. The children sing,

Shellycoat, Shellycoat, gang awa' hame,
I cry na yer mercy, I fear na yer name

On rare occasions, a shelleycoat will hide his shells under large rocks, at port or upon the decks of ships. If you find a shelly's coat, grab it! Many a Clan Chieftain will be sure to give you a good price.

One such bogle resides at Ettrick Water in the Borders, but it is certainly not as mischievous as the one at Leith!

Trow

A spaewife is a female elder of the
community with known psychic ability.

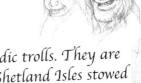

*T*rows are the descendants of Nordic trolls. They are believed to have arrived on the Shetland Isles stowed away on Viking dragon boats.

Known locally as the Grey Folk, these strange-looking creatures live in mounds (hadds) such as Trowie Knowe. They have pointed ears, knobbly feet and long wiry hair. They are never seen in the daytime, for sunlight casts them into standing stones. Trows can only be seen by the local spaewife.

Trows are very musical indeed. They have contributed greatly to Shetland's rich musical heritage. It is thought many the fiddler learnt trowie reels from hearing them sing. 'Aith rant', a well-known example was once heard at a trowie mound at the bay of Aith Voe.

Trows love thunder, Thor's anger! It reminds them of their homelands and they are often spotted dancing in a storm. They also like to bathe their baby trows by streams and lochs, especially the place known as Trolladale Water.

Aith's Rant

Baobhan Sith

Slains Castle, Aberdeenshire is the seat of the Earls of Erroll, Chiefs of Clan Hay.

If you are travelling alone by night, beware of the baobhan sith, Scotland's vampire ghosts. These demented women, alluring in their green translucent dress, always travel in groups. They dwell in glens at night waiting for their prey, young male travellers. After inviting the men to dance, they attack with razor-sharp nails hidden beneath their heavy velvet cloaks.

Beware of very beautiful women with glowing green eyes. They have the ability to fly like the wind, wild like the night. The only defence you will have is iron, so always hide a horseshoe in your pocket when out walking the glens.

A host of baobhan sith are said to often meet at Slains Castle perched on the cliffs of Cruden Bay on the North East coast. On the rooftop of this gothic pile, they descend usually causing chaos on this castle of the dead. To the dread of the Earl, the vampires often raid the magnificent library, feeding their thirst for rare antique books and knowledge. This coven feeds on local fishermen and marvels at the ghosts of shipwrecks rising from the haar of the sea.

Iron is your only protection.

Loireag

Below the mists of Beinn Mhòr, the highest
mount of South Uist, there dwells the loireag.
She is a water nymph of great age, a strange elf
woman. An old hag by accounts, not of this world.

The great love of this lonesome creature is music.
She listens often to the waulking songs (Orain
Luaidh) of the island women supervising
this final stage of beating the tweed. The
local lassies do not tolerate the loireag.
She has been known to spoil or even
steal the wool if waulkers sing out
of tune or time.

The loireag has a fine voice herself.
She is often seen flying in the skies on
her old tweed sack. Her haunting Gaelic melodies
drifting through the night air …

Mhorag Of Mordhobhar

Scotland's mountains, shores and glens hold many secrets, but 'tis' the deep lochs that harbour misty monsters of differing sorts. In the depths of Loch Morar, the deepest of lochs, there dwells a creature of considerable age, Mhorag of Mordhobhar.

Morag, a serpent-like creature, is said to move through the water as a 'cnap dubh' – a black heap. When the full moon hits the loch her streaming red eyes illuminate the waves and she often takes to sleep on one of the loch's islands, Eilean nam Breac.

Sightings date back to 1500, with twenty sightings in the last five years.

Legend has it that Morag can also take the form of a 'lady of the loch', an omen of death for the old MacDonalds of Morar. On such an occasion her constant wailing disturbs the local children greatly.

Dugall MacDonald of Clanranald MacDonald spotted the monster in 1510, and vowed to 'rid the land of the tairible beast'.

Loch Morar is the deepest freshwater loch in the British Isles. Its name, derived from the Gaelic, mordhobhar, means big water. It is to be found in Lochaber, West Highlands.

Linton Dragon

Linton Tower was destroyed by King Henry VIII during his Rough Wooing of 1543-1549. I have found mention of an ecclesiastical site at Linton Kirk dating to 1127.

I discovered the genealogical manuscript belonging to the Somerville/ Drum family (1680) in the Advocates Library, Edinburgh.

Dragons are not native to this land; they are few and far between. Only one has been recorded, the Dragon of Linton, a beast of fierce reputation who terrorised the Border lands in the twelfth century.

Nestled in a golden egg, the Linton Worm was brought to these shores by Viking warriors. This green mottled beast with emerald eyes lived in a cave on Linton Hill in a place still known as Wormeston.

Terror reigned until 1174, when a certain John de Somerville, of Norman descent, killed the dragon in a joust attack. Igniting the end of his lance with a wheel of flaming peat, he thrust it down the beast's throat. The spiral indents noticeable in the hill today were carved by its writhing in pain.

In length, three Scots yards, and somewhat bigger than an ordinary man's leg, with a head more proportionable to its length than greatness. It had its den in a hollow piece of ground, a mile south east from Lintoun Church, it destroyed both men and beast that came its way
(Somerville - Drum family manuscript, 1680)

Sir John Sommerville was appointed Royal Falconer and titled the first Barrone of Lintoune. To this day the Sommerville crest bears the heraldic dragon and Linton Tower became the clan stronghold for centuries to come. It is said the teeth of Scotland's last dragon are hidden in a secret underground passage that connects the tower and Linton Kirk. The legend was carved into the Somervail Stone, the tympanum above the doorway of the Kirk. One of the finest Norman carvings in Scotland, it may even survive from the time of the dragon. Depicting the knight battling against two dragons, the appearance of a second creature remains a mystery.

The wode Laird of Laristone
Slew the worm of Worme's Glen
and wan all Linton parochine.

Hogboy

Time has almost forgotten the Orcadian hogboy. He is truly ancient, a goblin mound-dweller with knobbly skin and bulging deep-set eyes. Paid in kind with gifts of milk, oats and butter, the hogboy was known to protect the nearby farms. However, to approach a hogboy mound alone was dangerous. The temper of the grey creature was often known to flare, especially if he thought you were after his golden hoard.

The name is derived from the old Norse word, 'haug-bui' meaning mound farmer. The name was given to ancestral spirits of burial mounds, 'haugr', connected to farms. When the Vikings settled on the Isles they transferred their myth to explain these strange indigenous creatures habiting the many mounds of the Orcadian landscape.

On my travels, I once visited the famed tomb of Maeshowe. Alive in local memory, it was thought this monument was once home to a rather cantankerous hogboon. Venturing inside, I found no evidence of the hogboy. Discovering Nordic runes carved all over the walls, I believe Vikings broke into the tomb sometime in the twelfth century. From deciphering the runes, I fear they stole the hogboy's great treasure. It is not clear if the incised drawing of a dragon is hogboy or Viking graffiti.

The Old Norse name for Maeshowe was 'Orkahaughr' as featured in the Orkneyinga Saga. (12th century)

Maeshowe is a monumental chambered tomb, one of the great Neolithic treasures in Europe. Some antiquarians have suggested an age of over 5000 years old. Hidden within the tomb, carved upon its walls, is one of the most significant collections of rune carvings.

It was long ago that a great treasure was hidden here. Happy is he
that might find that great treasure. Hakon alone bore treasure from
this mound

It is surely true what I say that treasure was taken away treasure was
carried off in three nights before those
Runes from Maeshowe (12th-century)

�619ᛁᛁᛆᛁᛗᚹᛘᛁᚼᛁᚱᛁᛏᚿᛒᚢᛒᚱᚿᚢᚳᛁᛁᚼᛁᛁᛁᛁᛁᚱᛁᛁᛒᚱᛁᛏᛁᛁᛁᛇᛁᛁᚱᚿ

Lady Of Sandwood Bay

*T*he most wondrous place I ever set eyes upon is Sandwood Bay on the far North West coast.

Of staggering beauty with its white sparkling beach, cliffs and windswept dunes, this place is remote and wild.

It is no wonder then that this remote bay is home to a ceasg, a Scottish mermaid. Visitors have often noted the eerie atmosphere of the place. I have felt it myself, although I have never seen her.

For the haar often lifts and reveals the Lady of Sandwood, Isabella, a mermaid of astounding beauty. She is seen often singing ancient melodies of the mist on the bay's rock stack, Am Buachaillie.

She was recently seen in the water by a local fisherman who reported her as 'large-bosomed with pearls flowing through her wild red hair'.

Scottish mermaids are of course the most beautiful. Covered head to toe with scales of silver and silk, they shimmer in the water.

Unlike other Scottish sirens that draw sailors to the fate of the rocks, Isabella of Sandwood is a shy and gentle creature, but she will raise the seas if you disturb the peace of her bay.

It is believed if a 'maighdean na tuinne' (maid of the wave) is ever caught, she may grant three wishes ...

Selkie

Selkies are the beautiful seal folk of the North. On shore they shed their seal-skins to reveal their attractive human form. From basking on the rocks, they dance on sandy shores. To see them move in the moonlight and wind.......

Guard their sealskins they must. If they are stolen by mortals, a selkie will be land-bound forever and obliged to marry the thief.

On a visit to North Uist in the Outer Hebrides, I came across the tale of the McCodrums. Many years ago a fisherman named McCodrum stole a sealskin and married a selkie. They were happily married with children, but the selkie wife always longed for the sea. Many years later her daughter discovered her sealskin locked in a carved chest. In an instant, her mother, clutching her skin, fled to the beach. She left her family for the sea, but always returned when the moon was at bay to swim with her babes in the waves. Descendants of this family became known as the McCodrums of the Seals (Clann Mhic Codruim nan rón).

If a woman sheds seven tears of loneliness into the sea, a male selkie lover shall she find.

With moonlight, I hear the music of the sea
and I need to dance. I smell the salt and I
long to be with my ain folk swimming in those
dark cold waves. The longing rocks me, a Selkie
I will always be. The water in ma heart, the
waves in ma soul
McCodrum

Cù Sìth

The cù sìth is the fairy dog of the Highlands, a huge hound that haunts the glens of the North. If you sense this shadowy canine walking beside you, never engage his stare, for he has the green eyes of death. This deadly harbinger, usually associated with large houses or castles, is bound by its territory. It haunts the 'daoine duchasach', the hereditary people of the place and its howl can be heard for miles around.

Urisk

The urisk is a rather gruesome type of brownie that dwells in water. This hairy, solitary creature can only be seen by those with second sight. They are much intrigued by humans, but they can never befriend due to their frightening form. Some say the urisk has the legs of a goat, surely the strangest of Scotland's beasties.

Fated to live forever alone in the lochs and streams, shunned by the other fairies of this land, the urisk longs always for friendship.

If you know a urisk lives on your estate, seek him out, he will prove a true friend and trusted companion.

Ben Venue in the Trossachs is the most famous retreat of these elusive beasties. They meet for festivities in a corrie high in the crags above Loch Katrine. This rocky amphitheatre is known as 'Coir na Uriskin', Goblin's Cave.

In the shadow of the Cuillin mountains, a urisk lurks often in the crystal clear waters of the enchanted Fairy Pools on the Isle of Skye. Secreted away in the most beautiful of watery worlds.

Treading the
water with his
long staff, lonely,
lonely as can be ...

King Otter

There is no creature more prized than the King Otter (rìgh nan dòbhran). Also known as the water dog, it is rarely seen. It is a majestic beast, a giant with the strength of a hundred of its kind. The Otter King is always accompanied by seven black otters. His fur, silver it gleams.

This elusive beast is hunted only by the bravest of men. They waste years searching for its hidden holt, a magnificent wooden den. A splendid jewel upon its head possesses magical powers which provides great protection in any circumstance.

The beast can only be killed by hitting the white spot below its chin. Many a ghillie has been taken by its fierce jaws.

Ghille – Estate/Game keeper

Be warned, it is fearsome
indeed.

Glaistig

Glaistig is derived from the Gaelic
(glas – grey & stig – sneaking)

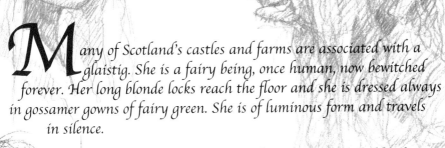

Many of Scotland's castles and farms are associated with a glaistig. She is a fairy being, once human, now bewitched forever. Her long blonde locks reach the floor and she is dressed always in gossamer gowns of fairy green. She is of luminous form and travels in silence.

The glaistig is of great use on farms and households; she can set herself to hard labour. Being somewhat stubborn, this witch has her own mind. It proves beneficial to reward services with an offering of milk left in a Glaistig Stone.

The appearance of a glaistig often foretells an event within a house. Only then will she be glimpsed in the gloaming. With the destruction of a property, her screeches haunt the air.

Most Highland folk are pleased to share homes with a glaistig; she is of great strength. But never anger her – the rearrangement of your furniture every night will prove intolerable to your lady.

A glaistig was associated with the House of Lamont at Ardnadrochit, Mull. When reivers came to steal the cattle at a place known as Heroes' Hollow, she transformed the herd into stone. Distraught at the loss of her cattle, she was consumed by grief and died soon after. The herd of boulders on the hill can still be seen.

The glaistig greatly fears dogs, especially terriers, her form they see instantly.

Brownie

The Scottish brownie (brùnaidh) is a common household spirit. Attached to many a Highland household, in exchange of subsistence of milk and oats, brownies will carry out general chores. After a hard day's work, they can be found snoring in the hay bales of nearby barns.

They have the appearance of tiny old men (bodachan sabhail), with few clothes and untameable brown hair.

As shocking as a naked brownie can be, never clothe or name one. Taking great offence, they will leave immediately. However, offering a gift of clothes is a good trick if you are trying to get rid of a troublesome brownie but beware, they may curse your land.

Scottish brownies are incredible storytellers, wee blethering beasties. They will mesmerise you with legends of old.

There was a well-known brownie called Puddlefoot who lived at Clochflodich farm near Pitlochcry. He loved to splash in Allt-Mor waterfall and often left his signature muddy footprints all around. One day he discovered his name when someone called to him on the old road to Dunkeld. The loved Puddlefoot left forever.

Puddlefoot, Puddlefoot,
Come awa hame,
We're sorry for the namin',
We'll nae do it again.

A brownie known as Aitken Drum lived at the village of Bladnoch, Galloway. He was known to sing on the bridge, but he too has long gone. What I would give to hear again, the voice of Aitken Drum!

Finfolk

Of all seal folk of the water, the Finfolk of the Orkney Isles are the most feared. These dark sorcerers of the seas terrorise the local shores.

When storms are at bay, the Finman lurks lonely in his longboat, sealskin clad, just waiting to take. They travel to land to kidnap humans, eternal partners they seek. The bane of the fishermen – never approach their territory, they will induce great damage to your vessels.

Marked by the sign of the seal, these wizards of the north also control the seas and storms. They can wish themselves to different places and can travel far distances with only a few strokes of the oar.

It is believed the Finfolk are in some way descended from the magic Finns of northern Norway, the Sami. Many moons ago, the Sami People were infamous for their magic powers, mysterious sea-people indeed.

The fishermen speak of Folkfolkaheem, their glitterin' underwater kingdom, a magnificent palace of coral, pearl and gold. Within the waves, the music of the sea surrounds their secret winter retreat. In summer months they live on disappearing islands that rise in and out of the mist, the most famous being Hildaland.

The Stanes O' Odin are a pair of ancient monoliths located near the Stones of Stenness.

There is a tale of a local, Guidman O' Thorodale who managed to glimpse Hildaland by looking though the hole of the Odin Stone. Stepping ashore he broke its ancient spell and renamed it 'Eynhallow', the Holy Isle. You can visit this mystical island and wonder at the ruins of the twelfth-century church.

Eynhallow Fair, Eynhallow free
Eynhallow sits in the middle o' the sea
A roaring roost on every side,
Eynhallow sits in the middle o' the tide.

The FinFolk have one weakness, white metal. They are obsessed with silver. Local fishwives always keep a silver charm on them, in case of attack.

People still search for the last remaining disappearing island of Hether Blether … its spell still to be broken.

His boat is made from seal skins or some kind of leather, he also hath a coat of leather upon him, and he sitteth in the middle of his boat, with a little oar in his hand, fishing with his lines, and when in a storm he sees the high surge of a wave approaching, he hath a way of sinking his boat, till the wave pass over, least thereby he should be overturned.
(John Brand, A New Description of Orkney, 1703)

Giant Of Bennachie

Bennachie, the great mount of Aberdeenshire is still home to one of our most formidable giants, Jock O' Bennachie. He is one of the original giants of this ancient region. Upon the mountain, he dried his massive shirts on a rock at Craigshannoch and slept in a stone bed known as Little John's Length.

From the peak of Mither Tap he watched that great battle of Mons Graupius. After long consideration, he eventually intervened, defending the Caledonians against the Romans. Following the Caledonian defeat, he rescued their leader, Calgacus, but did also loot much treasure!

Jock O' Bennachie fought endlessly with the other local giants, especially the ogre that lived on the mountain of Tap O' Noth. He often bombarded his mountain with massive boulders. His handprint is still visible on the monolith, the Gouk Stane. In retaliation, Jock's enemy sent a local witch, disguised as a beautiful Caledonian princess. With a fated kiss, he fell asleep under his mountain. The sleeping hero still awaits, only one can release him. An iron key hidden on the heather hill is still to be found, dictated in the Scottish prophecy:

'Scotland will never be rich, be rich,
Till they find the keys of Bennachie,
They shall be found by a wife's ae son, wi ae e'e, (only son with one eye)
Aneath a juniper tree.'
Thomas the Rhymer (1220-1297)

A fresh and unconquered people, never
likely to abuse our freedom, show
forthwith at the very onset what
heroes Caledonia has in reserve.
Speech by Calgacus before
battle – Agricola by Tacitus
(De vita et moribus
Iulii Agricolae ad 98)

The Scottish mountain range of the Grampians takes its name from the
Battle of Mons Graupius, reputed to have taken place on Bennachie
c. AD 83 (Beinn na Ciche – Hill of the Breast).

The peaks of Mither Tap and Tap O' Noth both command impressive
Iron Age forts.

Blue Men

When sailing the Minch, a dangerous strait in the Outer Hebrides, beware of the Blue Men.

With skin of shimmering blue, these strange beings stare with faces of ash grey. They control these local shores and are said to dwell in underwater caves, the largest belonging to the Blue Men Chief.

If you enter the 'Sruth nam Fear Gorma' (Stream of the Blue Men) there will be anger in the waves and they will chase your vessel with great speed.

Only seen from the waist upwards, they curse and scream. Never take one onboard, they will wreck your vessel; many ships have been taken.

My family have always paid homage to the Men of the Minch. A poem of old has come down through the ages; if sung onboard, you will be granted safe passage.

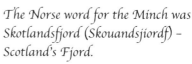

The Norse word for the Minch was Skotlandsfjord (Skouandsjiordf) – Scotland's Fjord.

Dalriada (Dál Riata) is the name of the ancient kingdom of the Scots (Scotti) – Western Isles.

In trusted waters, let me be,
I sail and pay homage to the sea,
Your glitterin' home, a marvel of Alba
The secret treasure of ancient Dalriada.

Bean Nighe

The Bean Nighe, the 'washing woman', is a devilish fairy of the North.

This witch, stout and awful, washes the linen of those about to die in remote pools and streams. If you catch sight of her through the trees, the blood-stained clothes are sure to be yours. However, if caught unaware, she will be forced to foretell your future.

If you hear the stone-beating of the washing of clothes, flee if you can. If the Bean Nighe sees you first, she will paralyse you senseless.

By moonlight she hangs her bloody washing on the trees, garments dripping in the breeze ...

Brownie De Boisgelin

My dear good friend, the Marquis de Boisgelin informs me of some foreign fairy dwelling on his fine estate in Brittany. This Scots brownie of sorts sings the old Scottish songs and yearns for the hills of home. It is believed Merlin captured him and brought him to his homeland centuries ago. He escaped from La forêt de Brocéliande, Merlin's magic wood near Rennes. The Marquis grants him haven in his secret labyrinth.

In gratitude, he often leaves a barrel of precious whisky at the entrance of the manoir. His best friends, an owl and a hawk, nest in the long avenue of trees. Helpful in the way brownies are, he gathers holly from the enchanted forest and bottles mist from the loch.

Les korrigans, the fairy locals prove unfriendly, but they suffer his participation in the fairy Fest Noz, the Breton night dance. This Scots brownie loves the Celtic music; it reminds him of home.

I promise the next time I visit this beautiful place, I will pop him in my sporran and finally take him home.

Paimpont Forest near
Rennes is said to be the
Arthurian La forêt de
Brocéliande. In this magical
forest lies the final resting
place of the famous wizard,
le Tombeau de Merlin.

Fachan

Stone carved balls are archaeological curiosities particular to Scotland. These elaborate carved balls are mostly found in the North East. They are thought to date from the Neolithic-Bronze Age. Their function remains mysterious.

*I*n my youth, I visited the stunning Glen Etive in search of the fachan. I saw movement in the heather-lined glen, but its ugly form I did not witness. A creature of curiosity, this dreaded beastie is particular to the West Highlands. A dwarf of sorts with one eye, arm and leg.

Black feathers sprout from its head, with a mouth terribly wide. He is of great strength and often takes to destroying ancient pockets of pine with his agate club. The fachan guards the Vran Trio, three mysterious carved stone balls, their powers unknown.

His dwelling and treasure lies between the Herdsmen of Etive, the two great mountains to the North.

The Dwarf of Glen Etive will do you no harm. I am sure he is content to live in such astounding beauty.

Nuckelavee

The 'Mither o'the Sea' is an ancient Orcadian
Goddess, the spirit and force of the summer seas.

*S*o feared is the nuckelavee of the Orkney Isles,
I am reticent to describe, so I present a poem
of old:

> *A devil of the sea, skinless and dripping flesh,*
> *A sea monster terrible, a centaur with fins,*
> *Gaping jaws ready to take,*
> *His Cyclopic eye burns with flames.*
>
> *Come ashore for rack and ruin,*
> *Havoc it brings, disease and drought.*
> *With killer breath, he blows Mortasheen –*
> *A disease to strike horses of this land.*
>
> *The burnin' of seaweed, the kelp it dements,*
> *Ready for rampage, only one can halt its rage,*
> *the Celtic enchantress,*
> *Mither o' the Sea.*

Take heed, crossing fresh water is
your only defence against the
nuckelavee ...

Redcap

*T*he least said the better! A creature of ill repute, of unthinkable horrors. Often present in my childhood nightmares, those haunted nights so far away.

He is a murderin' terrible goblin who attacks travellers who dare enter his evil abode. He frequents many castles of the Borders, namely the ominous Hermitage Castle built by Lord Soulis in the thirteenth century.

This Borders beast obsessively guards his morbid treasure, hoards of victims' possessions. His cap drips sodden with their blood.

Never hope to outrun the dreaded Redcap. His heavy boots of iron never weigh him down. There will be no escape from his sharp pikestaff. Stay clear of the Hermitage.

Heather Pixie

*I*n the gloamin' across the many heather glens, they swarm in the skies, thriving in the heather of home ...

The reelin' heather pixies with the dancin' Thistle King ...

The gloaming is the Scottish twilight – a time of magic when our beasties do appear.

Pentland Imp

This imp who dwells in the Pentland hills, large of form, tends to follow lovers on their romantic trysts.

Distracted by picnics, a passionate kiss, or loving embrace, it stalks walkers and steals whatever it can.
It is particularly fond of jewellery, chocolate and sweet buns.

Mrs Jeanie Robertson, from the village of Corstorphine in Edinburgh, sighted the imp around 1710: 'a braw wee beast, I ever did see'.

Identifiable by its long ears, the Pentland imp will never steal from a redhead – it's terrified of them!

The Pentland range of hills is situated in Midlothian. The area takes its name from the legendary King Loth, King of the Goddodin people, one of his forts of course being Dun Eidyn, Edinburgh.

Schiehallion

The Robertson Clan Chief always takes the forename of Struan. The Robertsons of Strowan are descended from the Celtic Earls of Atholl.

The 'Clach na Bratach', the Robertson Clan heirloom, has oracle and healing powers and is carried only by the Clan Chief.

*S*chiehallion, the 'Fairy Mountain of Caledonia' dominates Clan Roberston lands in Highland Perthshire. Scotland's mystical mountain, this powerful place resonates at the very geographical heart of Scotland. It is the pride of the Robertsons of Strowan, the oldest and most royal of clans.

Standing proud between Loch Rannoch and Loch Tummel, its views cast over the wild and rugged Rannoch Moor and beyond. It is no wonder this magnificent setting is the ancestral home of Scotland's fairies and the majestic dwelling of the Caledonian Fairy Queen. With her astounding beauty, she can only be seen by the Chiefs of Clan Robertson and she will always aid their defence. It is believed she forged the Robertson charm stone, the 'Clach na Bratach', from the crystal quartz of the misty mountain-top. In the possession of Clan Donnachaidh (Robertson) since 1315, this relic of antiquity is used for healing and predicting the future. This Stone of the Standard is also carried in battle, but if it clouds over or cracks inside, the Clan Chief should begin to worry.

Travellers swarm to the site hoping to catch a glimpse of the Queen. A cave at the place known as Tom a Mhorair provides entry to the stone mountain palace, but once it closes behind you, the secret door shuts forever.

Few have gained entry to the stone palace. A Robertson clan piper once entertained the fairies of Schiehallion for seven days; when he returned he was seven years older. The Fairy Queen keeps safe the Book of Struan, an account of all tales, songs and legends relating to THE Clan.

Virtutis Gloria Merces –
Glory is the reward of valour
– Robertson Clan motto

This is a glaistig that once lived on my estate. The kindest creature I have ever known, I called her by the name Seonag. My most trusted advisor, walking and talking in the gloaming, I sought her guidance on many matters. She left years ago to aid the Forresters of Corstorphine Castle at Edinburgh. I do not know of her present whereabouts. If you have seen her, please ask her to write. The large painting of this pencil study hangs proud in my grand hall. My most treasured portrait, my most beloved of beasties.

John, Lord Dunteviot, Great Clan Chieftain

Dunteviot Library

A New Description of Orkney, Zetland, Pightland-Firth and Caithness, by John Brand, 1703 Edinburgh, printed by G.M and sold in London by J. Taylor at the ship in St. Paul's Churchyard.

The Orkneyinga Saga, Codex Flateyensis, Royal Library of Copenhagen.

Descriptio Insularum Orchadiarum, by John Ben, 1529, Robertson-Forrester Archives, Corstorphine Castle, Edinburgh.

The Kingis Quair, by James the First, King of Scotland (1394-1437), 15th c., Bodleian Library, Oxford.

The Historie of Foure-Footed Beasts, by Edward Topsell, 1607, Innerpeffray Library, Perthshire (est.1680).

Lament for the Makaris, William Dunbar, 1500 ('Gentill Roull of Corstorphine'), Ex Libris John Lord Dunteviot.

RELEASE OF PRESS
NATIONAL TREASURE DISCOVERED IN EDINBURGH

On 11th July will be Published

COMPLETE IN ONE VOLUME WITH
OVER THIRTY ILLUSTRATIONS

THE BOOK OF BEASTIES

BY

LORD DUNTEVIOT

July 11th 1807, Edinburgh

A national treasure has been discovered within the deepest vaults of the Robertson Archives, Edinburgh.

Written by Lord Dunteviot in 1710, *The Book of Beasties*, is recognised as one of the earliest compilations of Scottish myth and legend.

This record of Scottish myth includes illustrations that are unique, mysterious and strange. Please note the pristine condition of both book and fine drawings. Many of the accounts of beasts include footnotes of historical significance.

It has been decided by the Council of Chiefs to publish this rare manuscript for the general public so that they too will learn from such a fine contribution to Scottish heritage. The original copy will be auctioned next week at *Thursday's Salerooms* on George Street, Edinburgh.

This Celtic masterpiece was the first of a series of volumes written by the Great Clan Chieftain.

Containing valuable snippets of Scottish history, this sketchbook mentions often the prized artefacts and places of astounding beauty of this country.

Hailed as one of the most important Scottish artistic discoveries in recent years, *The Book of Beasties* has survived to tell its story.

A bestiary without compare, *The Book of Beasties* will appeal to all.

The publishers beg to inform the Public and the Trade that THE BOOK OF BEASTIES, complete in one volume, will be ready for delivery on the 11th of July

Price, neatly bound in cloth........£1 1 0

(Gilt edges and marble leaves may be had at all Publishers)

AUTHOR

BELLE ROBERTSON

Known to many as the *Treasure of the East*, folklorist and writer, Robertson grew up on the Forrester lands at the *Cross of Torphin* in Edinburgh. From the Celtic School at the University of Edinburgh, she has travelled extensively throughout Scotland and Brittany recording myths, legends and songs.

ARTIST

LARRY MACDOUGALL

MacDougall, one of the leading fantasy illustrators lives and works in Ontario, Canada. Descended from the MacDougalls of Dumfries, South West Scotland, he continues to honour his ancestral homeland by dedicating his life to illustrating the magical and mysterious. Ever on the search of new otherworldly creatures, he loves to roam the Niagara Escarpment which runs through his hometown of Hamilton.